DEVOTIONAL PRAYER JOURNAL

Jane L. Fryar

P9-CCS-499

Forgiven & FREE

cta
Christ to All

The vision of CTA is
to see Christians highly effective
in their ministry so that Christ's Kingdom
is strengthened and expanded.

Forgiven & FREE

Jane L. Fryar

Copyright © 2020 CTA, Inc.
1625 Larkin Williams Rd.
Fenton, MO 63026
www.CTAinc.com

ISBN: 978-1-947699-68-7
PRINTED IN THAILAND

Getting Started

Freedom! It's the dream of many. The daughter sitting for days at her dad's bedside as he struggles with pneumonia. The junior-high student watching the clock in her classroom creep ever so slowly toward the end of the school day. The sixty-something HR professional counting down the days to retirement.

Which of these people are free? Are any of them? How would you know?

How about you? Are you free right now? Truly free? If not, what needs to end—or begin—before freedom is a personal reality? Once you have that freedom, how do you plan to use it? And where does your relationship with the Lord Jesus fit in with all this?

This journal is designed to help you explore those questions—and answer them!

As you use it, keep your Bible close. Plan to highlight significant passages and perhaps memorize some of them. As you write, engage in an ongoing conversation with Jesus, your Savior. Ask him to keep on revealing to you through his Word what it means to be forgiven and truly free.

The free gift of God is eternal life in Christ Jesus our Lord.
Romans 6:23

As far as the east is from the west, so far does he remove our transgressions from us.
Psalm 103:12

What turns a palace into a prison? Or vice versa? In other words, what are the barriers to true freedom? How about these: Worry? Sorrow? Fear? Guilt? Resentment? Meaninglessness?

How would it free your heart to know *for sure* that you are included in the *our* and *us* of Psalm 103:12?

Freed by Forgiveness

Draw a cross on a sticky note. Affix the note to an east wall. Imagine walking, running, driving, or flying straight east. No matter how far you go, you will never catch up with west. In Jesus, your sins are gone. You are free from them!

He was wounded for our transgressions, crushed for our iniquities; upon him was the punishment that made us whole, and by his bruises we are healed.
Isaiah 53:5 NRSV

Sin. It's such an icky word. Instead, we would rather "mess up," "bungle," or "botch." But the Bible always makes our true diagnosis (and its cure) quite clear: we sin, but because of Jesus, God forgives. Circle each *our, us,* and *we* in Isaiah 53:5. Where do you see yourself in this verse?

Freed by Forgiveness

God's forgiveness is free, but it was certainly not cheap.
Read more about the price Jesus paid in Mark 15.

*To [Jesus] all the prophets bear witness
that everyone who believes in him receives
forgiveness of sins through his name.*
Acts 10:43

Many people picture God as a tyrant intent on ruining their fun and keeping them enslaved. When is it hardest for you to believe your Lord has your best interests in mind? Write about a time like that. What brought you back around to rest in the truth the Bible reveals?

Freed by Forgiveness

Someone has said, "Feelings make fine servants but terrible masters." Our feelings can trick us into believing we are guilty when, in fact, God's Word promises the freedom of full forgiveness. Pray for wisdom so that your feelings serve you well but never master you.

There is therefore now no condemnation
for those who are in Christ Jesus.
Romans 8:1

Read Romans 8:1–11. Underline the words *now* and *no* in Romans 8:1. Then write a few sentences about each of these two words. Finally, ask yourself, "What did I just learn about freedom?"

Freed by Forgiveness

Do you regularly carry a shoulder bag, backpack, or briefcase? Over the next few days, pay special attention as you set it down. In your heart, thank Jesus for freeing you from the burden of your sin—a load much, much too heavy for you to carry.

Be kind to one another, tenderhearted, forgiving one another, as God in Christ forgave you.
Ephesians 4:32

Write about a time you found it hard to forgive someone who wronged or hurt you in some way. How did this grudge limit your freedom? Was the final outcome God pleasing or is the Holy Spirit still at work in the situation?

Free to Forgive

Sometimes, the Holy Spirit softens our heart by leading us to do something kind for someone we resent. Think about an act of kindness you could do, perhaps anonymously, as you recall God's boundless love for you in Christ.

Let everyone be quick to listen, slow to speak,
slow to anger; for your anger does not
produce God's righteousness.
James 1:19–20 NRSV

Quick to listen. Slow to speak. Slow to anger. How does each of these create more freedom? Slow to listen. Quick to speak. Quick to anger. How does each of these restrict your freedom?

Free to Forgive

Righteousness—right standing with God—already belongs to you, his forgiven child, by faith in Jesus. Reminding yourself of that truth will set you free, will make you quick (and slow) in all the right ways.

Put on then, as God's chosen ones, holy and beloved, compassionate hearts, kindness, humility, meekness, and patience, bearing with one another and, if one has a complaint against another, forgiving each other; as the Lord has forgiven you, so you also must forgive. And above all these put on love, which binds everything together in perfect harmony.
Colossians 3:12–14

The lifestyle described in Colossians 3:12–14 doesn't come naturally to us. It comes supernaturally, though, as we rely on the Holy Spirit to work it in us. Think about these words. Then write about the increased freedom this kind of lifestyle offers us as God's children.

Free to Forgive

As you get dressed each day this week, imagine yourself putting on the "new clothes" you have been thinking and writing about.

The fruit of the Spirit is . . . joy.
Galatians 5:22

"Buy more stuff. Have better experiences." That's the recipe for happiness suggested by all those pop-up ads on our phones. The Bible, though, points us in a quite different direction. Christian joy is the contented confidence that "God's got this"— no matter what "this" is. Write about the freedom this joy brings.

Freed for Joy

List 12 things that make you smile—puppies, a walk in the rain, your favorite song, for example. Thank God for giving these to you. Then thank him for the joy of knowing his forgiveness in the cross of your Savior.

The joy of the LORD is your strength.
Nehemiah 8:10

The joy that belongs to us in Jesus has very little to do with circumstances. When life is easy, God is good—and his joy is ours. When times are hard, God is good—and his joy is *still* ours. Write about the joy the Holy Spirit worked in you during an easy time in your life, then a hard time.

Freed for Joy

What's the hardest thing you will do today or this week?
Remember, the joy of the Lord is your strength even then! Copy
Nehemiah 8:10 on a sticky note and post it on your refrigerator.
Let it remind you that you are free to be joyful—and, thus,
strong—in the Lord.

You make known to me the path of life; in your presence there is fullness of joy; at your right hand are pleasures forevermore.
Psalm 16:11

Think about a time you experienced deep, contented joy and peace. What made that experience so fully satisfying? What might be blocking the contented joy Jesus wants you to have continually in your everyday life? Think about Psalm 16:11 as you write.

Freed for Joy

Note that Psalm 16:11 is not a promise for the future. It's a description of present reality—a reality available to you right now. Joy is yours for the asking. So ask already!

Do not be anxious, saying, "What shall we eat?" or "What shall we drink?" or "What shall we wear?" For . . . your heavenly Father knows that you need them all. But seek first the kingdom of God and his righteousness, and all these things will be added to you.
Matthew 6:31–33

In Matthew 6, Jesus mentions several issues human beings commonly worry about. List them. Then add your own top three worries to the list. Jesus wants you to be worry-free. How do his words in verses 31–33 point the way to that outcome?

Worry-Free

Read Matthew 6:25–34 from your Bible. What additional comfort do you see there? Jot down one way you will put these words into practice today.

Blessed are those who trust in the LORD,
whose trust is the LORD. They shall be like a
tree planted by water, sending out its roots by the
stream. It shall not fear when heat comes, and its
leaves shall stay green; in the year of drought it is
not anxious, and it does not cease to bear fruit.
Jeremiah 17:7–8 NRSV

Drought brings hardship in many farming communities still today, just as in Bible times. For most of us, though, "the year of drought" has little to do with sparse rainfall. Write a letter to yourself about a personal "dry time." How did the Lord sustain you *in* that anxious time and ultimately bring you *out* of it?

Worry-Free

Make a copy of the letter you just wrote. Add one or more encouraging Bible verses from this journal to it. Put it in a safe place. Find and read it whenever you start to become anxious.

Do not be anxious about anything, but in everything by prayer and supplication with thanksgiving let your requests be made known to God. And the peace of God, which surpasses all understanding, will guard your hearts and your minds in Christ Jesus.
Philippians 4:6–7

Philippians 4 offers two specific, practical remedies for worry: 1) Ask for what you need (supplication) and 2) thank God for the help that is on the way. With that in mind, write about a current worry—large or small. Imagine your heavenly Father looking over your shoulder, reading the requests you are making and the thanks you are giving.

Worry-Free

Call or text a prayer partner. Offer to pray for her worries and ask her to pray for yours. Share the promises of Philippians 4:6–7.

Do nothing from selfish ambition or conceit, but in humility count others more significant than yourselves.
Philippians 2:3

True, godly humility is simply self-forgetfulness. Knowing God's forgiving love for us in Jesus frees us to focus on others. Jesus will see to it that our own needs are met! List five small ways your life will be different today as a result of realizing this. Then make any specific plans necessary to bring these changes about.

Freed for Self-Forgetfulness

Your name is already written in the Book of Life (Philippians 4:3)!
God himself is—right now!—your Father (1 John 3:1)! You are
forgiven and free to live today like the child of heaven you truly
are! Bask in that!

Let each of you look not only to his own interests, but also to the interests of others. Have this mind among yourselves, which is yours in Christ Jesus.
Philippians 2:4–5

In our culture, it is amazingly easy to live a self-absorbed, self-focused life. But then, it has always been easy in every human culture. As God's own people, forgiven and dearly loved, we have been freed from that kind of oppression. We have the mind of Christ! What difference does that make?

Freed for Self-Forgetfulness

Look for an opportunity today to pause and listen attentively to someone in your sphere of influence. Focus just on that person— not on planning your response or sharing your own experience. Notice how this approach can transform a relationship.

Now the full number of those who believed were of one heart and soul, and no one said that any of the things that belonged to him was his own, but they had everything in common.
Acts 4:32

Living in community with the first Christians must have been thrilling! Our Lord wants us to enjoy the same freedom from selfishness, from self-focus, that the Holy Spirit worked in Jesus' first followers. As you write now, ask God to work it in you. (Get as specific as possible.)

Freed for Self-Forgetfulness

If at times you fail to live out the self-forgetful lifestyle Jesus has given you, don't be surprised. Even the great apostle Paul struggled! (Romans 7 describes that struggle.) Confess your sins to your heavenly Father, leaving them at the foot of Christ's cross. Remember, you are forgiven and free!

Be still, and know that I am God.
Psalm 46:10

For some of us, the time goes too quickly—in part, because we go too quickly. Life is one big rush, one great blur. For others, time goes too slowly. We are bored or seduced by one meaningless activity after the next. Psalm 46:10 speaks to either and both of these circumstances. How does it speak to you?

Free to Slow Down

Read Ecclesiastes 3:1–8. How can the wisdom the Holy Spirit shares here help you grow more comfortable in your relationship with time, busyness, and purpose?

[Jesus] said to them, "Come away by yourselves to a desolate place and rest a while." For many were coming and going, and they had no leisure even to eat.
Mark 6:31

As you read Mark 6:31, imagine yourself as one of Jesus' followers. You've just heard his invitation. In your thoughts, accept the invite and go with him. Write about what that would have been like. What would you have seen, heard, smelled, touched, experienced?

Free to Slow Down

Today, eat at least one meal slowly and in the peaceful presence of your Savior. You are free to slow down and enjoy your Savior's presence. Jesus says so!

Now may the Lord of peace himself give
you peace at all times in every way.
The Lord be with you all.
2 Thessalonians 3:16

Just think! "Peace at all times" and "in every way"! Rushing or resting, you live in the Lord's presence. His peace is his gift to you. If you took full advantage of that, how would your life be freer, fuller?

Free to Slow Down

Write a thank-you note to Jesus for his gift of peace and the freedom it brings. Then, in a safe container or your barbeque grill, burn it. As you watch the smoke ascend, imagine it being the incense of thanksgiving from your heart to the heart of your Savior.

So, whether you eat or drink, or whatever you do, do all to the glory of God.
1 Corinthians 10:31

What do you see as your life's mission or purpose? What kinds of differences has our Lord invited you to make? Do these differences feel more like "have to's"? Or "get to's"? Explain.

Free to Live on Purpose

Memorize 1 Corinthians 10:31. As you work on memorization, personalize the meaning of the words in your own life. What does it mean to you as a daughter, mom, sister, wife, neighbor, or co-worker?

Whatever your task, put yourselves into it, as done for the Lord and not for your masters, since you know that from the Lord you will receive the inheritance as your reward; you serve the Lord Christ.
Colossians 3:23–24 NRSV

Dwell on the word *whatever* in Colossians 3:23–24 for a few moments. How does this passage inject meaning into even the most mundane tasks of life? How can living with purpose in this way make for an exciting life?

_____
_____
_____
_____
_____
_____
_____
_____
_____
_____
_____
_____
_____
_____
_____
_____
_____
_____
_____
_____
_____
_____
_____

Free to Live on Purpose

Write the word *whatever* on half of a note card and decorate it.
Fold the card to make a tent and put it on your bedroom dresser.
As you begin and end each day, let it remind you of your life's
purpose—you serve the Lord Christ!

You were called to freedom. . . . Only do not use your freedom as an opportunity for self-indulgence, but through love become slaves to one another. For the whole law is summed up in a single commandment, "You shall love your neighbor as yourself."
Galatians 5:13–14 NRSV

How can we be "called to freedom" and, at the same time, "slaves to one another"? What kind of freedom is that? Think and write about it.

Free to Live on Purpose

We are forgiven and freed by our Savior to live a purposeful, meaningful life. Remind yourself of that by creating a personal mission statement in three brief sentences. Use it to guide you as you make decisions at home, work, and church. Revisit it after a few months and revise, if that seems wise.

> *There is no fear in love, but perfect love casts out fear.*
> *1 John 4:18*

Jesus' love is perfect. It is complete, absolute, unconditional, and total. Fear flees in the face of this kind of love. When and where do you experience fear? How might you immerse yourself more deeply in Jesus' love, drawing upon it for confidence when you are afraid?

Free from Fear

Close your eyes and picture yourself confronting the thing that makes you most afraid. Now see Jesus—your mighty, risen Savior— standing beside you. Slowly repeat the words of 1 John 4:18 three or four times. Watch peace increase and your fear flee.

Surely God is my salvation; I will trust,
and will not be afraid.
Isaiah 12:2 NRSV

Salvation is a richly meaningful word. It speaks first of the forgiveness of sins Jesus won for us on Calvary's cross. But it also contains every benefit that flows from that forgiveness. _Wholeness_ might be a good synonym. List as many of these benefits as you can. How does knowing God as your salvation banish fear?

Free from Fear

Use your favorite Bible app or website to find all the "surely"
verses in Psalms or in the New Testament. The word *surely* acts
as a kind of exclamation. It highlights certainty. Which is your
favorite "surely" promise? Memorize it! Or post it somewhere you
will see it often.

For I, the LORD your God, hold your right hand; it is I who say to you, "Fear not, I am the one who helps you."
Isaiah 41:13

Take an imaginary walk before you begin to write. Picture Jesus holding your right hand as you walk together. Write about that experience. How does the promise of Isaiah 41:13 scatter your fears?

Forgiven & Free

Look for a way to hold hands with a loved one sometime this week. Notice the sense of love and safety this simple act brings. Share the promise of Isaiah 41 and its meaning with that person as you encourage each other in God's faithfulness.

The free gift of God is eternal life in Christ Jesus our Lord.
Romans 6:23

Look back over this journal. What fresh insights have you gained as you reflected on the forgiveness and freedom that is ours in Jesus? How has your confidence grown, confidence that belongs to you as one of God's daughters, a member of his very own family? List those insights here.

Forgiven & Free

Take one more look at what you have recorded in this journal.
Put a star next to three of your favorite Scripture verses, insights,
or activities. Plan a way to share one of these with your mother,
daughter, friend, or sister in Christ in the days ahead.

To see all of CTA's devotion books and journals, visit us at www.CTAinc.com. You may order online or by calling 1-800-999-1874.

If this book has made a difference in your life or if you have simply enjoyed it, we would like to hear from you. Your words will encourage us!

Email: editor@CTAinc.com; include the subject line: FFWXXPJ

Write: Editorial Manager, Department FFWXXPJ
CTA, Inc.
PO Box 1205
Fenton, MO 63026-1205

Comment Online: www.CTAinc.com (search FFWXXPJ)